The Complete
PANCHATANTRA

Sandhivigraha   Harmony and Strife

Retold & illustrated by
Bujjai

© Bujjai
First published 1999
Second impression June 2000

Published by
Devamala Books Pvt Ltd

III Floor Zenofer Tower
No 119/2 Jawaharlal Nehru Road
Jafferkhanpet
Chennai 600083
Phone 3711824 3711825
Fax 0091 44 3712332
e-mail msmgroup@satyam.net.in

Designed by Krishna Shastri
Processed by Bee Vee Graphics, Chennai
Printed by Vadapalani Press,
AVM Compound, Vadapalani, Chennai 600026

To Lakshmi, my wife,
Who, for forty years,
stood by me through my struggles,
encouraged me in all my endeavours,
and left me and my children
suddenly two years ago,
I dedicate these books

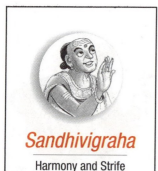

Sandhivigraha

Harmony and Strife

MEGHAVARNA WAS THE KING OF CROWS.

IN A CAVE CLOSE TO MEGHAVARNA'S HOME LIVED UPAMARDA, THE KING OF OWLS, ALONG WITH HIS FOLLOWERS. THE TWO KINGS WERE MORTAL ENEMIES...

AT NIGHT, UNDER COVER OF DARKNESS, UPAMARDA AND HIS FOLLOWERS WOULD FLY TO MEGHAVARNA'S PLACE AND KILL THE CROWS.

MEGHAVARNA GATHERED HIS COUNSELLORS TOGETHER.

FRIENDS, OUR ENEMY IS CUNNING AND THEREFORE POWERFUL...

HE STRIKES AT NIGHT WHEN WE CAN'T SEE, AND IN THE DAY, HE DOESN'T VENTURE OUT.

SO, MY WISE FRIENDS! HOW SHALL WE DEAL WITH HIM? LET UDDEEPI SPEAK FIRST.

O, KING! HE IS A POWERFUL ENEMY. LET'S MAKE PEACE WITH HIM.

A CLOUD CAN'T STAND AGAINST THE WIND. HE WHO BOWS HIS HEAD BEFORE THE STRONG IS SAFE.

WHAT IS YOUR OPINION, SANDEEPI?

Sandhivigraha

Harmony and Strife

Sandhivigraha

Harmony and Strife

VENERABLE ONE! YOU'RE THE OLDEST AND THE WISEST AMONG US ALL. PLEASE GIVE US THE BENEFIT OF YOUR COUNSEL.

YES. EVERY SUGGESTION HAS ITS OWN MERIT BUT NOT ONE OF THEM IS SUITABLE NOW.

THEREFORE?

DUPLICITY ALONE SERVES OUR PURPOSE NOW!

BE OPEN AND FRANK WITH YOUR GOD AND YOUR TEACHER. THE REST YOU MAY DECEIVE!

WHEN THE ENEMY IS CRUEL AND CUNNING, DUPLICITY IS OUR ONLY COURSE. TRY TO FIND THE ENEMY'S WEAKNESS AND DESTROY HIM.

HOW? WE DON'T EVEN KNOW WHERE HE LIVES!

OUR SPIES CAN UNCOVER HIS HIDE-OUT AS WELL HIS WEAK POINTS. SPIES ARE, AFTER ALL, THE EYES OF A KING.

HOW CAN THEY GO ABOUT THIS WITHOUT RAISING SUSPICION?

DISGUISED AS SALESMEN, MADMEN, SNAKE-CHARMERS AND SO ON.

SIR! WHAT IS THE ORIGIN OF THE ENMITY BETWEEN CROWS AND OWLS?

Sandhivigraha
Harmony and Strife

HOW DID CROWS AND OWLS BECOME ENEMIES? HMM. LET'S SEE. LONG, LONG AGO, ALL THE BIRDS GATHERED TOGETHER IN COUNCIL...

WHAT IS THE GOOD IN HAVING GARUDA AS OUR KING? HE NEVER SPARES US A MOMENT FROM HIS SERVICE OF GOD VISHNU.

HE DOESN'T EVEN LISTEN TO OUR PRAYERS WHEN WE'RE IN TROUBLE!

AVOID A DULL TEACHER, AN UNBELIEVING PRIEST, AN INDIFFERENT KING, AND A SHARP-TONGUED SPOUSE!

YES! TRUE! CORRECT!

LET THE OWL BE OUR KING. HE LOOKS WISE AND RESPONSIBLE.

THE BIRDS MADE GRAND ARRANGEMENTS FOR THE CORONATION CEREMONY, WITH GARLANDS AND FESTOONS, AND A GREAT FEAST OF NUTS AND FRUITS. SUDDENLY, A CROW ENTERED, CAWING LOUDLY...

WHY HAVE YOU ALL GATHERED HERE? WHAT IS ALL THIS FESTIVITY ABOUT?

YOU KNOW WE HAVE NO KING WHO LOOKS AFTER OUR INTERESTS. SO WE'VE DECIDED TO MAKE THIS OWL OUR KING.

KA! KA! KA! HOW FOOLISH! THERE ARE SO MANY BEAUTIFUL, CLEVER BIRDS! WHY HAVE YOU CHOSEN THIS UGLY CREATURE WHO CAN'T FACE THE LIGHT?

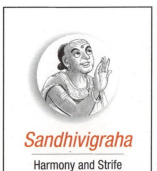

Sandhivigraha

Harmony and Strife

WHO IS THIS CROW? HE'S INSULTING ME!

THIS OWL IS UGLY AS WELL AS CRUEL. IF YOU MAKE HIM YOUR KING, YOU'LL BE RUINED.

WILL YOU REPLACE THE MIGHTY GARUDA WITH THIS GOOD-FOR-NOTHING FELLOW? KA! KA! KA!

JUST MENTIONING YOUR KING'S NAME SHOULD MAKE YOUR ENEMIES SHUDDER!

SHALL I TELL YOU THE STORY OF SILEEMUKHA, THE RABBIT?

DO!

ONCE UPON A TIME, AN ELEPHANT KING LIVED IN A FOREST WITH HIS RETINUE. HIS KINGDOM WAS THEN IN THE GRIP OF DROUGHT...

WE'RE DYING OF THIRST. THERE'S NOT A DROP OF WATER ANYWHERE!

O KING! IF IT CONTINUES LIKE THIS, WE'LL ALL PERISH.

GO AT ONCE TO THE EIGHT CORNERS OF OUR KINGDOM AND LOOK FOR WATER!

EIGHT ELEPHANTS SET OUT AT ONCE IN EIGHT DIFFERENT DIRECTIONS IN SEARCH OF WATER...

Sandhivigraha

Harmony and Strife

Sandhivigraha
Harmony and Strife

VIJAYA THE RABBIT STARTED OFF ON HIS MISSION...

THERE HE IS, WITH HIS HERD!

AN ELEPHANT IS NO LESS DANGEROUS THAN A SERPENT OR A TIGER. I MUST APPROACH HIM WITH CAUTION!

I'LL CLIMB THIS TREE TO BE SAFE!

GLORY TO THE MIGHTY ELEPHANT KING!

WHO CALLS?

WHO ARE YOU AND WHAT BRINGS YOU HERE?

I'M THE ENVOY OF THE GLORIOUS MOON!

I'LL BE FRANK WITH YOU, SIRE, IF YOU EXTEND YOUR ROYAL PROTECTION TO ME!

YOU'RE SAFE. SPEAK UP!

THE MOON CHARGES YOU WITH TRESPASSING ON HIS SACRED LAKE, AND WITH ACTS OF AGGRESSION AGAINST THE RABBIT RACE WHICH HE PROTECTS.

HE FORBIDS YOU FROM GOING TO THE LAKE!

WE'RE NOT BOUND BY HIS ORDERS!

MY KING PROMISES TO NOURISH YOU AND YOUR FOLLOWERS WITH AMRUTA, THE ETERNAL MOON LIGHT, IF YOU DO AS HE BIDS YOU!

IF NOT, HE WILL WITHDRAW HIS LIFE-GIVING MOONLIGHT, AND THEN ALL OF YOU WILL BE SCORCHED BY THE SUN AND PERISH!

Sandhivigraha
Harmony and Strife

I ADMIT MY ERROR. LET NOT THE WRATH OF THE MOON DESTROY US. GUIDE US, DEAR ENVOY! WHAT SHOULD WE DO?

O KING! FOLLOW ME, THEN, ALL ALONE.

VIJAYA TOOK THE ELEPHANT KING TO THE LAKE OF THE MOON.

SIR, BEHOLD OUR MIGHTY KING, THERE HE IS!

I SHALL BEG HIS PARDON!

SO SAYING, THE ELEPHANT KING KNELT DOWN, DISTURBING THE WATER OF THE LAKE...

O KING, WHAT HAVE YOU DONE? THE MIGHTY MOON IS ANGRY! SEE HOW A THOUSAND MOONS SURROUND YOU!

WHY IS HE ANGRY WITH ME? I'VE COME JUST TO BEG HIS PARDON!

YOU SHOULDN'T HAVE TOUCHED THE SACRED WATER AND ROUSED HIS ANGER!

I BESEECH YOUR KING FOR FORGIVENESS! I SWEAR THAT I AND MY FOLLOWERS WILL NEVER COME TO THIS LAKE AGAIN!

WE'LL NEVER TOUCH THIS WATER. NEVER!

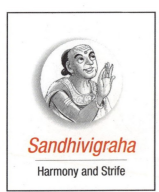

Sandhivigraha

Harmony and Strife

Sandhivigraha

Harmony and Strife

Sandhivigraha
Harmony and Strife

HE IS A ROGUE, DISGUISED AS A SAINT. HE IS THE ENEMY OF RABBITS.

THEY SUSPECT ME. I MUST WIN THEIR CONFIDENCE!

O SUN GOD! LOVE, KINDNESS AND RIGHTEOUSNESS ALONE ARE TRUE! ALL ELSE IS UNTRUE, MERE MAYA.

BROTHER RABBIT! HE SEEMS TO BE A PIOUS AND RIGHTEOUS BEING, A SAINT. LET'S REFER OUR CASE TO HIM.

OH, HE IS A DEVIL QUOTING THE SCRIPTURES. WE MUST BE WARY! LET'S QUESTION HIM FROM A SAFE DISTANCE!

O, LEARNED SAGE! WE BEG YOU TO MEDIATE IN OUR DISPUTE. WHOEVER IS FOUND GUILTY SHALL BE EATEN UP BY YOU!

INNOCENT FRIENDS! YOU'RE MISTAKEN. I'M NOT A DEVIL. KINDNESS TO ALL CREATURES IS MY MOTTO!

DEAR CHILDREN, I'M OLD AND DEAF. COME NEAR ME...

...AND TELL ME WHAT YOUR DISPUTE IS ABOUT. **COME CLOSE!**

Sandhivigraha
Harmony and Strife

I'M DEAF, YOU SEE! EACH OF YOU, PLEASE SHOUT YOUR CASE INTO MY EARS.

COME ON! DON'T HESITATE!

THE CROW ENDED HIS STORY THUS:

THE POOR CREATURES TRUSTED THE CAT, FELL INTO HIS CLUTCHES, AND WERE KILLED.

SO, YOU SEE, IF YOU TRUST A WICKED FELLOW, YOU'LL MEET THE SAME FATE AS THE RABBIT AND THE PARTRIDGE!

THINK IT OVER AND DO AS YOU PLEASE!

WHAT HE SAYS SEEMS TO BE TRUE...

HE IS RIGHT!

HE IS A SENSIBLE FELLOW!

WE SHOULDN'T BE HASTY!

THEN THE BIRDS FLEW AWAY TO THEIR HOUSES LEAVING BEHIND THE OWL WHO COULDN'T GO HOME BECAUSE IT WAS DAYTIME...

WHERE **IS** EVERYBODY? IT'S ALL SILENT HERE! WHY THIS DELAY IN CROWNING ME? **WHY?**

MY LORD! THIS CROW HAS PREVENTED YOUR CORONATION CEREMONY. ALL THE BIRDS HAVE GONE AWAY...

WHY? YOU RASCAL OF A CROW! YOU'VE RUINED ME! HENCEFORTH WE'LL BE MORTAL ENEMIES!

Sandhivigraha

Harmony and Strife

YOU AND I WILL NEVER LIVE IN PEACE AGAIN!

THE WOUND MADE BY AN AXE ON A TREE DISAPPEARS, BUT THE WOUND MADE BY CRUEL SPEECH IS NEVER HEALED.

I HAVE UNNECESSARILY BROUGHT ABOUT ENMITY WITH THE OWLS.

WORDS, CRUEL AND CARELESS, CONDEMN HIM WHO HAS SPOKEN THEM.

YOU MUST BE CAREFUL WITH A FOE UNNECESSARILY MADE. AFTER ALL, YOU WOULDN'T TAKE POISON JUST BECAUSE A DOCTOR IS YOUR NEIGHBOUR...

EVEN TRUTH SHOULD BE KEPT BACK IF, BY SPEAKING, YOU HURT PEOPLE.

THE OLD CROW FINISHED HIS NARRATIVE...

AND THAT'S HOW THE ENMITY BETWEEN OWLS AND CROWS STARTED!

LEARNED SIR! WHAT DO YOU ADVISE NOW?

EVEN NOW THERE IS A WAY TO OVERCOME THE ENEMY.

PLEASE TELL US HOW!

I'LL DECEIVE AND DESTROY HIM!

HOW IS THAT POSSIBLE?

Sandhivigraha

Harmony and Strife

YOU'LL KNOW HOW I CAN DESTROY THE ENEMY IF YOU LISTEN TO THIS STORY FIRST!

ONCE, A BRAHMIN WAS RETURNING TO HIS VILLAGE, CARRYING ON HIS SHOULDERS A GOAT FOR SACRIFICE.

THREE ROGUES SAW HIM ON HIS WAY HOME...

AHA! BROTHERS! **LOOK!** WHAT A FAT GOAT HE'S CARRYING!

IF WE CAN ONLY GET IT FROM HIM, WE COULD MAKE A GOOD MEAL OF THE ANIMAL!

LET'S TRICK HIM!

SOON, ONE OF THE ROGUES ACCOSTED THE BRAHMIN.

DEAR SIR, WHAT ARE YOU DOING?

YOU'RE CARRYING A DOG ON YOUR SHOULDERS? DON'T YOU KNOW THAT ONE SHOULDN'T TOUCH A DOG, A HANGMAN AND A DONKEY? AND YOU, A BRAHMIN, TO DO THIS?

NONSENSE, YOU'RE BLIND! THIS IS A **GOAT**, NOT A DOG.

HA! HA! HA! DO AS YOU PLEASE, SIR!

THE BRAHMIN CONTINUED ON...

STRANGE! WHAT DO I SEE?

Sandhivigraha
Harmony and Strife

Sandhivigraha

Harmony and Strife

LISTEN CAREFULLY. CATCH HOLD OF ME AS IF BY FORCE. BEAT ME, SMEAR BLOOD ON MY BODY, AND DRIVE ME OUT OF YOUR TERRITORY.

THE ENEMY'S SPIES SHOULD THINK THAT I'VE BETRAYED YOU AND THAT I'M BEING DRIVEN OUT OF YOUR KINGDOM.

AND THEN?

YOU SHOULD SHIFT YOUR BASE FROM THIS PLACE TO YONDER MOUNTAIN.

MEANWHILE, I'LL WIN THE ENEMY'S CONFIDENCE AND FIND OUT WHERE HE LIVES.

HOW WILL YOU DO THAT?

DON'T YOU KNOW OWLS ARE BLIND IN THE DAYTIME?

NOW, GET READY! WE'LL CARRY OUT OUR PLAN!

YES, SIR!

YOU'RE NOT WORTHY OF BEING KING! YOU'RE DULL AS WELL AS OBSTINATE!

WHAT, YOU DARE INSULT A KING? **TRAITOR!**

THERE IS SOMETHING VERY INTERESTING HAPPENING WITH THE CROWS.

LET'S WATCH!

THE ATTENDANTS OF THE CROW-KING RUSHED TO THE SPOT AND SURROUNDED THE OLD CROW...

TRAITOR!

Sandhivigraha
Harmony and Strife

STAY AWAY. DON'T KILL HIM! I WANT TO PUNISH THE RASCAL!

HIS LIFE SHOULD BE MADE MISERABLE.

MEGHAVARNA PRETENDED TO PECK AT THE OLD CROW AND SMEARED HIM WITH BLOOD...

GUARDS! TAKE HIM AWAY FROM HERE, AND PUSH HIM OFF THE BANYAN TREE!

FOOLS! YOU'LL PAY FOR THIS!

MEANWHILE... WE MUST IMMEDIATELY REPORT THIS TO OUR KING!

AFTER SOME TIME, THE CROW KING AND HIS FOLLOWERS FLEW TO THEIR NEW MOUNTAIN BASE, LEAVING THE OLD CROW BEHIND.

IN THE COURT OF THE KING OF THE OWLS...

SO HIS CHIEF MINISTER HAS DESERTED HIM AND HIS DEFENCES ARE VULNERABLE.

WE'LL ATTACK THE CROWS THIS VERY NIGHT!

UPAMARDA, KING OF THE OWLS, SET OFF WITH HIS VAST ARMY...

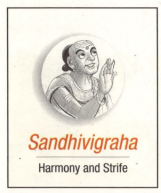

Sandhivigraha

Harmony and Strife

THE ARMY OF OWLS APPROACHED THE BANYAN TREE...

NOW, CHARGE!

KILL! KILL! KILL THE ENEMY!

STRANGE! THERE'S NOT A SINGLE CROW IN SIGHT!

STOP, STOP! YOU FOOLS!

THERE ARE NO CROWS HERE AT ALL! WE ARE FIGHTING WITH EACH OTHER!

HAIL, O MIGHTY CONQUEROR! VICTORY IS EVER YOURS! YOU ARE INVINCIBLE!

WE''VE CAPTURED THE FORTRESS OF THE CROWS, O KING!

SHUT UP!

STOP THAT SILLY FLATTERY! THE ENEMY HAS DUPED US!

WE MUST FIND HIM BEFORE HE GETS TO ANOTHER STRONGHOLD.

MEANWHILE, THE OLD CROW WAS OBSERVING THEIR MOVEMENTS...

THE TIME IS RIPE FOR MY INTERFERENCE. HAVING UNDERTAKEN IT, ONE SHOULDN'T LEAVE A MISSION UNFULFILLED! JAI GARUDA!

Sandhivigraha

Harmony and Strife

KA! KA!

WHOSE CRY IS THAT? IT'S THE ENEMY! SEARCH FOR HIM!

THE OWLS FOUND THE OLD CROW WOUNDED AND BLEEDING...

WHO'S THIS? KILL HIM!

PRAY, DON'T KILL ME.

I'M MEGHAVARNA'S MINISTER BUT I WAS DRIVEN OUT OF HIS KINGDOM BY HIM.

SPEAK UP!

YESTERDAY, I WARNED MEGHAVARNA NOT TO FIGHT WITH YOU.

THEN?

I ADVISED HIM THAT IT'S ALWAYS SAFE TO MAKE PEACE WITH AN ENEMY WHO'S STRONGER THAN YOU.

THEN?

THEN THE VILLAINOUS CROW BECAME FURIOUS WITH ME. HIS FOLLOWERS WOUNDED ME CRUELLY TILL I FELL DOWN, ALMOST DEAD.

FROM NOW ON, I'M AT YOUR SERVICE.

I WANT TO TAKE REVENGE ON HIM. I'LL DIRECT YOUR ARMY TO HIS FORTRESS. YOU CAN DESTROY THEM ALL!

THEN, UPAMARDA, KING OF THE OWLS, SUMMONED ALL HIS COUNSELLORS.

YOU'RE ALL WISE AND EXPERIENCED. TELL ME, WHAT IS TO BE DONE NOW? RAKTAKSHA, WHAT IS YOUR ADVICE?

PAY HEED TO MY COUNSEL, SIRE! KILL THIS CROW AT ONCE!

Sandhivigraha

Harmony and Strife

HE IS OUR ENEMY, SO WE MUST KILL HIM. WHAT DO THE WISE SAY?

"KILL THE ENEMY WHEN HE'S WEAK, OTHERWISE HE'LL GAIN STRENGTH AND BECOME A SOURCE OF DANGER."

HAVE YOU NOT HEARD THE STORY OF THE SNAKE WHO GAVE AWAY GOLD COINS?

ONCE UPON A TIME, THERE LIVED A BRAHMIN. ONE DAY, HE WAS TAKING A NAP UNDER A TREE IN HIS FIELD...

SUDDENLY...

WHAT DO I SEE? A SNAKE...!

HE MUST BE LORD SUBRAHMANYA! I'VE NEVER MADE AN OFFERING TO HIM. THAT'S WHY I'M NOT GETTING ANYTHING OUT OF THIS FARM!

THEN THE BRAHMIN HURRIED HOME AND RETURNED WITH A BOWL OF MILK...

LORD! FORGIVE ME FOR NOT HONOURING YOU ALL THESE DAYS...PRAY ACCEPT THIS OFFERING.

WHEN HE RETURNED THE NEXT DAY...

OH! OH! HOW KIND HE IS! HE HAS LEFT A GOLD COIN IN THIS EMPTY BOWL!

THE BRAHMIN USED TO OFFER MILK TO THE SNAKE EVERY DAY AND IN RETURN THE SNAKE GAVE HIM A GOLD COIN. ONE DAY...

DEAR SON! I'M GOING TO TOWN. EACH DAY, PLACE A BOWL FULL OF MILK NEAR THAT ANT-HILL TILL I COME HOME...

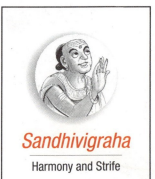

Sandhivigraha
Harmony and Strife

THE BRAHMIN'S SON DID AS INSTRUCTED BY HIS FATHER. HE TOOK A BOWL OF MILK TO THE ANT-HILL. WHEN HE CAME BACK THE NEXT DAY...

GOOD HEAVENS! A GOLD COIN!

THIS ANT-HILL MUST BE FULL OF THEM!

I'LL KILL THIS SNAKE AND GET THEM ALL!

THE NEXT DAY, HE BROUGHT SOME MILK AND PUT IT IN THE USUAL SPOT. THE SNAKE CAME OUT...

NOW I'LL KILL IT!

HE RAISED HIS STICK. BEFORE HE COULD BRING IT DOWN...

...THE SNAKE SPRANG AT HIM, AND KILLED HIM.

THE NEXT DAY, THE BRAHMIN RETURNED HOME AND LEARNT WHAT HAD HAPPENED...

BE KIND TO EVERY LIVING BEING. BE HOSPITABLE TO YOUR GUESTS!

HAVEN'T YOU HEARD THE STORY OF THE GOLDEN SWANS?

LET'S HEAR IT!

LONG, LONG AGO, THERE LIVED A KING, CHITRARATHA. IN HIS GARDEN WAS A BEAUTIFUL LAKE OF LOTUSES WHERE LIVED MANY GOLDEN SWANS...

Sandhivigraha

Harmony and Strife

EACH SWAN WOULD GIVE THE KING A GOLDEN FEATHER ONCE IN SIX MONTHS.

ONE DAY, ANOTHER BIRD CAME TO THE LAKE...

WHO ARE YOU? WHY ARE YOU HERE?

I'M GOING TO LIVE HERE WITH YOU!

NO, YOU CAN'T! WE'VE TAKEN LEASE OF THIS LAKE. EACH OF US PAYS A RENT OF ONE GOLDEN FEATHER EVERY SIX MONTHS TO THE KING.

THEN THE BIRD WENT TO THE KING...

O MIGHTY KING, THOSE SWANS IN YOUR LAKE ARE VERY ARROGANT.

WHY, WHAT HAVE THEY DONE?

THEY WOULDN'T LET ME LIVE WITH THEM IN THE LAKE.

THEY SAID "EVEN IF THE KING RECOMMENDS YOU, WE WON'T TAKE YOU!"

HOW DARE THEY SAY THAT! GUARDS! GO AND KILL ALL OF THEM AT ONCE!

Sandhivigraha

Harmony and Strife

AT THE LAKE...
LOOK! LOOK! THE KING'S GUARDS ARE COMING CARRYING SWORDS! SOMETHING MUST HAVE HAPPENED.

LET'S LEAVE THIS PLACE IMMEDIATELY!

THE BRAHMIN CONCLUDED HIS STORY THUS...
SO WE MUST BE GENEROUS TO EVERYONE.

THE NEXT DAY, THE BRAHMIN TOOK MILK AS USUAL TO THE ANTHILL.
O LORD SUBRAHMANYA! PARDON ME. MY SON PAID WITH HIS LIFE FOR HIS WICKED DEED.

PRAY ACCEPT THIS OFFERING...AND BE GENEROUS!

NO! LOVE ONCE LOST IS LOST FOREVER! TIES OF FRIENDSHIP ONCE BROKEN ARE FOREVER BROKEN.

RAKTHAKSHA CONCLUDED HIS STORY...
WE SHOULD THEREFORE KILL THE ENEMY EVEN THOUGH HE'S FRIENDLY!

NOW, WHAT IS YOUR OPINION, KROORAKSHA?

RAKTHAKSHA IS MISTAKEN. WE SHOULDN'T KILL SOMEONE WHO WANTS TO HELP.

DON'T YOU KNOW THE STORY OF THE DOVE WHICH SACRIFICED ITS LIFE?

THERE LIVED IN A FOREST A CRUEL HUNTER. HE WAS AS MERCILESS AS YAMA, THE GOD OF DEATH...

Sandhivigraha

Harmony and Strife

EVERYONE HATED THE HUNTER. ONE DAY...

THE SKY IS OVERCAST! A STORM IS ON ITS WAY...

WHAT A DOWNPOUR! WHERE WILL I FIND SHELTER?

THE HUNTER TOOK SHELTER UNDER A BIG TREE WHERE A PAIR OF DOVES LIVED...

GOOD GOD! WHAT HAS HAPPENED TO MY BELOVED WIFE? WHY HASN'T SHE RETURNED? SHE MAY HAVE LOST HER WAY IN THIS STORM!

HOW EMPTY AND DESOLATE THIS HOME IS WITHOUT HER!

A DEVOTED SPOUSE IS THE GREATEST BLESSING IN LIFE...

THE DOVE'S WIFE WAS ACTUALLY RIGHT UNDER THE TREE, TRAPPED IN THE HUNTER'S CAGE.

MY LOVE, I'M HERE. I'M PROUD TO BE YOUR WIFE! HUSBANDS AND WIVES MUST LIVE TO MAKE EACH OTHER HAPPY.

DEAR, LISTEN TO ME. BE HOSPITABLE TO A GUEST EVEN IF IT COSTS YOU YOUR LIFE.

THE GODS DON'T BLESS THOSE WHO ARE NOT KIND TO GUESTS!

DON'T BLAME THE HUNTER FOR TRAPPING ME. IT'S MY FATE. DON'T HATE HIM, HONOUR HIM. HE'S OUR GUEST.

SHE'S A VERY GOOD PERSON!

Sandhivigraha

Harmony and Strife

SIR, WELCOME TO OUR HOME. MAKE YOURSELF COMFORTABLE. WHAT CAN I DO FOR YOU?

CAN'T YOU SEE I'M SHIVERING IN THIS TERRIBLE COLD? DO SOMETHING!

THE DOVE BROUGHT SOME WOOD AND STARTED A FIRE.

OOHOOHOO! OHOOHOO! I FEEL BETTER NOW!

ARE YOU HUNGRY, SIR?

YES!

HOW CAN I FEED YOU? I CAN'T SATISFY YOUR HUNGER...

...AS I'VE NOTHING TO OFFER EXCEPT MYSELF.

SO SAYING, THE DOVE JUMPED INTO THE FIRE. THE HUNTER WAS STRUCK DUMB BY THIS WONDERFUL ACT OF SACRIFICE...

THIS NOBLE DOVE HAS OPENED MY EYES...

I NOW RENOUNCE ALL EARTHLY PLEASURES TO ATONE FOR MY SINS.

SO SAYING, THE HUNTER THREW AWAY HIS CLUB AND NETS, AND SET THE FEMALE DOVE FREE.

Sandhivigraha

Harmony and Strife

MY LOVE! HOW CAN I LIVE WITHOUT YOU! I MUST ALWAYS BE WITH YOU.

SO SAYING, THE FEMALE DOVE JUMPED INTO THE FIRE.

UP IN HEAVEN...

WHEREVER WE'RE TOGETHER, THAT IS HEAVEN...

THE HUNTER, PENITENT AND HEART-BROKEN, OFFERED HIMSELF TO THE FLAMES...

KROORAKSHA CONCLUDED THE STORY THUS...

THE DOVE GAVE HER LIFE TO HONOUR A GUEST; SO, WE SHOULDN'T KILL A GUEST, EVEN IF HE IS OUR FOE!

NOW, JWALAKSHA! WHAT IS YOUR ADVICE?

O KING! I AGREE WITH KROORAKSHA.

THERE ONCE LIVED A RICH OLD MERCHANT. WITH HIS RICHES, HE BOUGHT A POOR MAN'S DAUGHTER...

...AND MARRIED HER. SHE WAS VERY YOUNG.

O GOD! WHY ARE YOU SO CRUEL?

Sandhivigraha
Harmony and Strife

Sandhivigraha

Harmony and Strife

NOW, LET OUR WISE FRIEND VAKRANASA ENLIGHTEN US WITH HIS OPINION!

JWALAKSHA'S ADVICE IS GOOD. LET ME TELL YOU A STORY IN SUPPORT OF IT.

ONCE UPON A TIME, THERE WAS A POOR BRAHMIN WHO LIVED ON ALMS.

ONE DAY, SOMEONE FELT SORRY FOR HIM AND GAVE HIM TWO CALVES.

AFTER SOME TIME...

I'LL STEAL THESE CALVES TONIGHT!

HE SET OFF AT NIGHT TO THE BRAHMIN'S HOUSE...

WHO ARE YOU?

I'M SATHYAVADI, THE GHOST. WHO ARE YOU, AND WHERE ARE YOU GOING?

I'M A THIEF, GOING TO ROB A BRAHMIN OF HIS TWO CALVES.

REALLY? THEN LET'S GO TOGETHER AND...

I'LL EAT THE BRAHMIN UP!

AHHA...AHHA!

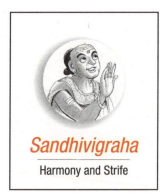

Sandhivigraha

Harmony and Strife

THE THIEF AND THE GHOST ARRIVED AT THE BRAHMIN'S HOUSE.

BROTHER GHOST! LET'S HIDE HERE TILL THE RIGHT MOMENT.

NOW THE BRAHMIN IS FAST ASLEEP, I'LL FINISH HIM OFF!

NO, THAT'S BAD! YOU MUST NOT EAT HIM TILL I STEAL HIS CALVES!

MY DEAR FELLOW! IF YOU TAKE AWAY THE CALVES FIRST, THEY MAY CRY AND WAKE UP THE BRAHMIN. THEN ALL IS LOST!

NO, NO! IF YOU ATTACK HIM FIRST, HE'LL WAKE UP AND ALL MY EFFORTS WILL BE IN VAIN!

THE THIEF AND THE GHOST BEGAN TO ARGUE LOUDLY AND HEATEDLY...

WHAT IS THIS COMMOTION? WHO ARE YOU BOTH?

MY DEAR SIR! THIS GHOST IS ABOUT TO EAT YOU!

SIR, HE'S A THIEF COME TO STEAL YOUR CALVES!

IS THAT SO? HRAAM! HREEM! HROOM! PHUT!

OH, NO, NO! PLEASE!

Sandhivigraha

Harmony and Strife

AWAY WITH YOU!

PLEASE! NO!

VAKRANASA ENDED HIS STORY...

DIFFERENCES AMONG OUR ENEMIES MAY SOMETIMES BE TO OUR ADVANTAGE, AS IN THE CASE OF THIS BRAHMIN!

SO WE SHOULD KILL THE OLD CROW!

WHAT IS YOUR ADVICE, PRAKARAKARNA?

THE OLD CROW NEED NOT BE KILLED.

LISTEN TO THIS STORY. ONCE THERE WAS A PRINCE IN WHOSE STOMACH LIVED A SNAKE...

HOW CAN I GET RID OF THIS SNAKE? THIS IS UNBEARABLE! I'LL LEAVE THIS COUNTRY.

SO THE PRINCE LEFT HIS COUNTRY IN DESPAIR...

THIS PLACE LOOKS PEACEFUL. I'LL STAY HERE.

NOW, THE RULER OF THAT CITY HAD TWO DAUGHTERS. THE ELDER DAUGHTER, WHENEVER SHE MET HER FATHER, BOWED TO HIM AND WISHED HIM GLORY AND VICTORY. THE OTHER WOULD SAY THAT HE WOULD GET WHAT HE DESERVED... ONE DAY, IN THE KING'S PRESENCE...

VICTORY TO YOU, O KING!

LET GOD BESTOW ON YOU WHAT YOU DESERVE.

Sandhivigraha

Harmony and Strife

Sandhivigraha

Harmony and Strife

IF THE POOR PRINCE KNEW THAT HE COULD KILL YOU BY DRINKING MUSTARD, HE WOULDN'T SUFFER LIKE THAT!

NO ONE KNOWS THAT A BIG TREASURE IS HIDDEN IN YOUR HOME. A POTFUL OF BOILING WATER POURED ON YOUR ANTHILL WILL FINISH YOU OFF!

THANK GOD!

I CAN NOW MAKE MY BELOVED HUSBAND HAPPY!

PRAKARAKARNA CONCLUDED HIS STORY THUS...

THE KING'S DAUGHTER, WHO OVERHEARD THE CONVERSATION OF THE SNAKES, POURED BOILING WATER ON THE ANTHILL AND KILLED THE SNAKE IN IT...

SHE THEN GAVE HER HUSBAND MUSTARD AND DESTROYED THE SNAKE IN HIS STOMACH.

SHE THEN LIVED HAPPILY WITH HER HUSBAND, AFTER TAKING THE TREASURE FROM THE ANTHILL.

LIKE THE SNAKE IN THIS STORY, THE OLD CROW MAY GIVE US VALUABLE ADVICE AS TO HOW TO GET RID OF THE ENEMY!

ALL RIGHT! THE OLD CROW SHALL LIVE!

BUT RAKTAKSHA DID NOT APPROVE OF THE KING'S DECISION.

ARE YOU REAL COUNSELLORS? YOU'VE MISLED THE KING. YOU'LL BRING DISASTER TO HIM AND HIS KINGDOM. THIS REMINDS ME OF A STORY.

Sandhivigraha

Harmony and Strife

THIS IS THE STORY OF THE FOOLISH CARPENTER...

ONCE, THERE LIVED A CARPENTER WHOSE WIFE WAS UNFAITHFUL TO HIM. ONE DAY, HE WAS SEIZED BY DOUBT...

I MUST FIND OUT THE TRUTH SOMEHOW!

MY DEAR, I'M GOING TO A NEARBY VILLAGE ON BUSINESS. I'LL BE AWAY FOR A WEEK.

THE NEXT DAY, THE CARPENTER LEFT HIS HOUSE...

NOW I'M FREE...I'LL SEND FOR MY OLD LOVER!

MEANWHILE...
I'LL WAIT HERE TILL NIGHTFALL AND QUIETLY RETURN HOME IN THE DARK.

THAT NIGHT... I'VE A KEY TO THIS BACK DOOR...

I'LL HIDE HERE AND WATCH!

MY GOD! WHAT A CHEAT HE IS!

Sandhivigraha
Harmony and Strife

HE'S HIDING UNDER THE BED! I MUST FOOL HIM.

THE LOVER ARRIVED...

I WAS WAITING FOR YOU. TODAY, AN ASTROLOGER CAME HERE AND PREDICTED THAT MY HUSBAND WOULD DIE SHORTLY.

MY GOD!

I WAS GRIEF-STRICKEN AND ASKED HIM HOW I COULD SAVE MY HUSBAND'S LIFE.

WHAT DID THE ASTROLOGER SUGGEST?

OH, MY GOD!

HE SAID THAT IF A STRANGER EMBRACED ME, THE CURSE WOULD PASS ON TO HIM AND MY HUSBAND WOULD BE SAVED...SO I INVITED YOU!

WHAT A FOOL I WAS TO SUSPECT HER.

O MY BELOVED HUSBAND!

I'M BLESSED TO HAVE YOU AS MY WIFE.

RAKTAKSHA CONCLUDED HIS STORY THUS...

THE FOOLISH CARPENTER WAS THUS DUPED BY HIS CLEVER WIFE. THE OLD CROW MAY ALSO BE CHEATING US. HE MUST BE KILLED!

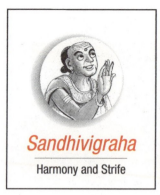

Sandhivigraha

Harmony and Strife

RAKTAKSHA'S ADVICE WAS IGNORED BY THE KING WHO SET THE OLD CROW FREE AND INVITED HIM TO BE HIS GUEST...

YOUR KINDNESS OVERWHELMS ME, SIR! PRAY, PROVIDE ME WITH SOME WOOD AND A FLAME.

RAKTAKSHA WAS CURIOUS...

WHAT FOR, SIR?

I WANT TO BURN MYSELF TO DEATH.

WHY, SIR, WHEN YOU'RE FREE AND A ROYAL GUEST!

MY SOLE DESIRE NOW IS TO BE REBORN AS AN OWL AND TAKE REVENGE ON MEGHAVARNA, THE KING OF CROWS.

MY DEAR SIR! EVEN AFTER BEING REBORN AS AN OWL, YOU WILL NOT LOSE THE NATURE OF A CROW. LISTEN TO THIS STORY...

THERE ONCE LIVED A GREAT SAGE IN A HERMITAGE ON THE BANKS OF THE HOLY GANGES...

HIS NAME WAS YAGNAVALKYA. ONE DAY, AS HE WAS PERFORMING HIS DAILY RITES, SOMETHING FELL FROM THE SKY INTO HIS OUT-STRETCHED HANDS.

OH! WHAT'S THIS!
A MOUSE MAID!

Sandhivigraha

Harmony and Strife

POOR CREATURE. NO, NO, DON'T BE AFRAID! I WON'T HARM YOU.

YOU'RE SAFE HERE. I SHALL COME BACK SOON!

HE THEN FINISHED HIS SACRED RITES AND RETURNED.

WHERE IS MY POOR LITTLE MOUSE...?...AH! THERE SHE IS!

THEN...

OM! OM! HROOM...

THE MOUSE WAS TRANSFORMED INTO A BEAUTIFUL LITTLE GIRL.

MY CHILD, COME WITH ME TO OUR HOME!

AT THE HERMITAGE...

MY DEAR! I'VE BROUGHT YOU SOMETHING WHICH WILL BE THE LIGHT OF YOUR EYES. IT WILL SATISFY YOUR LIFE'S DESIRE...

GOD HAS AT LAST GRANTED MY WISHES AND GIVEN ME A DAUGHTER...

THE GIRL WAS BROUGHT UP WITH GREAT LOVE AND TENDERNESS. ONE DAY...

IT IS TIME FOR OUR DAUGHTER TO MARRY.

Sandhivigraha

Harmony and Strife

LETS CHOOSE FOR OUR DAUGHTER A YOUNG MAN WHO IS WORTHY OF HER IN ALL RESPECTS.

AN ELIGIBLE BRIDEGROOM MUST HAVE SEVEN QUALITIES: WEALTH, BEAUTY, LEARNING, FAMILY TRADITION, YOUTH, STATUS AND GOODNESS.

LET HER CHOOSE HER OWN HUSBAND. I'LL FIRST INVITE THE GREAT SUN.

SO THE GLORIOUS SUN CAME DOWN...

HOLY SAGE! WHY HAVE YOU INVITED ME HERE?

MY DAUGHTER NEEDS A HUSBAND.

MY DAUGHTER! WILL YOU MARRY HIM? THIS IS THE SPLENDID SUN WHO LIGHTS UP ALL THE WORLDS!

NO, FATHER! I CAN'T BEAR TO LOOK AT HIM, HE IS TOO BRIGHT.

O BLESSED ONE, CAN YOU SUGGEST A BRIDEGROOM GREATER THAN YOURSELF FOR MY DAUGHTER?

YES, SIR! THE LORD OF THE CLOUDS IS GREATER THAN I...MY GLORY FADES WHEN HE COVERS ME.

THEN THE HOLY SAGE INVITED THE LORD OF CLOUDS HOME...

Sandhivigraha

Harmony and Strife

Sandhivigraha
Harmony and Strife

THE MOUSE IS MIGHTIER THAN I.

SO THE SAGE INVITED A MOUSE OVER....

O FATHER! HE IS SO VERY HANDSOME AND CHARMING!

DO YOU LOVE HIM, MY CHILD?

YES, FATHER! I'LL MARRY HIM. PRAY CHANGE ME INTO A MOUSE. WE'LL BE HAPPY TOGETHER!

RAKTAKSHA CONCLUDED HIS STORY THUS:

SO THE MIGHTY MOUNTAIN, THE GLORIOUS SUN, THE POWERFUL WIND AND THE GREAT CLOUD GOD COULD NOT ATTRACT THE MOUSE-MAID...

...WHO COULD NOT GO AGAINST HER NATURE. SO, EVEN IF YOU ARE REBORN AS AN OWL...

YOU'LL CONTINUE TO LOVE CROWS!

BUT NO ONE PAID ANY HEED TO RAKTAKSHA'S GOOD ADVICE AND THE OLD CROW WAS TAKEN AS A GUEST TO THEIR FORTRESS...

ONLY CLEVER RAKTAKSHA IS WISE AND DIPLOMATIC. I'M LUCKY...THE FOOLISH OWLS HAVEN'T TAKEN HIS ADVICE.

IN THE FORTRESS OF THE OWLS...

FRIENDS, TREAT HIM AS A ROYAL GUEST. HE IS OUR FRIEND AND WELL-WISHER.

Sandhivigraha

Harmony and Strife

LET THE OLD CROW CHOOSE WHICHEVER CHAMBER HE LIKES AS HIS HOME...

I MUST STAY NEAR THE GATE, NOT IN THE HEART OF THE FORTRESS...

...TO CARRY MY PLAN THROUGH!

I'M INDEED HONOURED BY YOUR KINDNESS, BUT I SHOULD NOT ABUSE YOUR HOSPITALITY. LET ME LIVE HERE BESIDE THE GATE.

AS YOU WISH!

THE OLD CROW WAS SUMPTUOUSLY FED AND GREW STRONG AND SLEEK...

THESE FOOLS TREAT THIS TREACHEROUS CROW LIKE A PRINCE!

O KING! LET ME WARN YOU AGAIN. YOU'RE BEING MISLED BY THESE FOOLISH COUNSELLORS. THIS REMINDS ME OF A STORY...

STOP YOUR WAGGING TONGUE!

LISTEN! ONCE UPON A TIME, A HUNTER WAS ROAMING ABOUT IN A FOREST IN SEARCH OF PREY...

WHAT DO I SEE? A BIRD LAYING A GOLDEN EGG! I CAN'T BELIEVE MY EYES...

I CAN MAKE A FORTUNE WITH THAT BIRD!

Sandhivigraha

Harmony and Strife

THE HUNTER CAUGHT THE BIRD AND PUT HER IN A CAGE.

IT'S DANGEROUS TO KEEP THIS BIRD WITH ME.

I'LL OFFER IT TO THE KING AND GET A REWARD.

IN THE KING'S PRESENCE...
PERMIT ME TO OFFER YOUR MAJESTY THIS RARE BIRD WHICH LAYS A GOLDEN EGG EVERY DAY.

AH! IT IS INDEED RARE! GIVE THE HUNTER A BIG REWARD!

SIRE! DON'T BELIEVE THE ROGUE. IT IS AN ORDINARY BIRD!

SO THE FOOLISH KING, ON THE ADVICE OF HIS FOOLISH COUNSELLORS, FREED THE BIRD. TO THEIR AMAZEMENT, SHE LAID A GOLDEN EGG AND FLEW AWAY...

ENOUGH OF YOUR NONSENSE! WE CAN JUDGE WHAT IS RIGHT AND WHAT IS WRONG.

RAKTAKSHA RESENTED THIS INSULT AND CALLED HIS FOLLOWERS TOGETHER...

FRIENDS! A GREAT CATASTROPHE IS GOING TO BEFALL OUR KING. IT IS FOOLISH TO REMAIN HERE ANY LONGER AND BE DESTROYED.

LET'S LEAVE AT ONCE FOR A SAFE PLACE, LIKE THE PRUDENT JACKAL WHO SAVED HIMSELF FROM DESTRUCTION...

Sandhivigraha

Harmony and Strife

ONCE, THERE LIVED A LION IN A FOREST. ONE DAY...

BAD LUCK TODAY. I HAVEN'T HAD A MORSEL OF FOOD!

THE HUNGRY LION, SEARCHING FOR FOOD, CAME TO MOUNTAIN CAVE...

AT NIGHTFALL, SOME ANIMAL MUST COME TO THIS CAVE FOR SHELTER AND PROVIDE ME WITH DINNER. I'LL LIE IN WAIT!

A SMART JACKAL LIVED IN THAT CAVE. AT THE CLOSE OF DAY, THE JACKAL CAME HOME. EVER PRUDENT AND ALERT, THE JACKAL SHOUTED...

O MY GOOD CAVE! HOW DO YOU DO? WHY ARE YOU SILENT TODAY?

HAVE YOU FORGOTTEN OUR UNDERSTANDING ABOUT EXCHANGING GREETINGS WHENEVER I RETURN?

I SEE...! MY PRESENCE HERE KEEPS THE CAVE MUM...I'LL IMITATE THE CAVE AND GREET THE JACKAL!

THUS THE FOOLISH LION GREETED THE JACKAL WITH A MIGHTY ROAR THAT SHOOK THE WHOLE FOREST...

AHA! AH! THIS IS THE FIRST TIME I'VE HEARD A CAVE TALK! HA! AH!

RAKTAKSHA CONCLUDED THE STORY THUS...

SO THE CLEVER JACKAL DETECTED THE PRESENCE OF A STRANGER IN HIS CAVE AND SAVED HIMSELF...

Sandhivigraha

Harmony and Strife

RAKTAKSHA SAID TO HIS COMPANIONS: LET US BE PRUDENT LIKE THE JACKAL AND LEAVE THIS FORTRESS BEFORE IT IS TOO LATE.

I'M GETTING OUT OF HERE. WHOEVER WISHES TO SAVE HIMSELF MAY COME WITH ME.

RAKTAKSHA AND HIS FOLLOWERS LEFT THE FORTRESS OF UPAMARDA, THE KING OF OWLS...

IT'S A GOOD THING THAT RAKTAKSHA HAS LEFT THE FORTRESS. HE ALONE IS SHREWD AMONG THE OWLS.

A KING MUST HAVE WISE COUNSELLORS, OR ELSE HIS DOWNFALL IS CERTAIN.

AFTER RAKTAKSHA'S DEPARTURE, THE OLD CROW BEGAN TO COLLECT PIECES OF WOOD FROM THE FOREST EVERY DAY...

WHY HAVE YOU PILED UP THESE LOGS HERE?

TO BUILD MY OWN DWELLING.

HOW EASY IT IS TO DECEIVE THESE FOOLS! HAH! HA!

AFTER SOME DAYS...

I'VE GATHERED ENOUGH WOOD TO DESTROY THE ENEMY. IT IS NOW DAYTIME AND THE OWLS ARE BLIND...I'LL FLY TO MY KING AND TELL HIM EVERYTHING IS READY.

IN THE PRESENCE OF MEGHAVARNA, THE KING OF CROWS...

O KING! NOW IS THE TIME TO ACT! LIGHT SEVERAL TORCHES AND FOLLOW ME TO THE FORTRESS OF THE OWLS.

Sandhivigraha

Harmony and Strife

O WISE ONE! PRAY TELL US HOW YOU ACHIEVED THIS!

THERE IS NO TIME TO TALK NOW. LET'S ACT FORTHWITH BEFORE OUR ENEMY NOTICES MY ABSENCE.

ALWAYS ACT QUICKLY AND FATE WILL FAVOUR YOU. DELAY BRINGS ILL-LUCK.

FOLLOW ME AND WE'LL DESTROY OUR ENEMY RIGHT NOW.

SO, MEGHAVARNA AND HIS RETINUE REACHED THE FORTRESS OF THE OWLS WITH BURNING TORCHES...

THROW THE TORCHES AT THE GATE, THERE IS A PILE OF DRY WOOD JUST BEHIND IT.

IN A MOMENT, THE FORTRESS OF THE OWLS WAS A BURNING HELL...

WHAT A CURSED FOOL I WAS NOT TO HEED THE GOOD ADVICE OF RAKTAKSHA! IT IS TOO LATE.

THUS THE OWLS PERISHED IN THE FIRE AND THEIR FORTRESS BURNT TO THE GROUND. MEGHAVARNA AND HIS RETINUE RETURNED AT LAST TO THEIR OLD HOME ON THE BANYAN TREE.

MY FRIENDS! THIS IS A DAY OF GREAT REJOICING FOR US. WE MUST ALL EXPRESS OUR GRATITUDE TO THE WISE AND VENERABLE CHIRANJIVEE!

WISE ONE, WE'D LIKE TO KNOW HOW YOU ACHIEVED THIS MAGNIFICENT SUCCESS.

Sandhivigraha

Harmony and Strife

O KING, LISTEN CAREFULLY! ONE MUST BE VERY CAUTIOUS AND EVER ALERT AMONG ENEMIES.

ONE MUST BIDE ONE'S TIME PATIENTLY PLAN EFFICIENTLY AND THEN STRIKE SWIFTLY...

EVEN THE INVINCBLE PANDAVAS HAD TO LIVE IN DISGUISE.

BUT LIVING IN THE ENEMY'S CAMP IS LIKE WALKING ON THE EDGE OF A SWORD...

YES! BUT ALL THE OWLS WERE FOOLS EXCEPT RAKTAKSHA. THEY PAID HEAVILY FOR TRUSTING THE ENEMY AND A STRANGER...LIKE THE FROGS WHO TRUSTED MANDAVISHA...

WHO IS MANDAVISHA?

A WICKED BLACK SNAKE. LISTEN TO HIS STORY!

ONE DAY...

I MUST GET MYSELF AN EASY MEAL TODAY!

AHA! HERE'S A POND FULL OF FROGS. I'VE AN IDEA...

THE SNAKE CRAWLED SLOWLY TO THE EDGE OF THE POND.

HALLO! MANDAVISHA! WHY ARE YOU DULL TODAY?

I'M SAD AND MISERABLE. A BRAHMIN HAS CURSED ME!

Sandhivigraha

Harmony and Strife

WHY DID HE CURSE YOU?

I WAS GOING ABOUT IN SEARCH OF FOOD YESTERDAY WHEN I SAW A FROG, LEAPT AT HIM AND STRUCK...

BUT, BY MISTAKE, I BIT A BRAHMIN BOY WHO DIED AT ONCE. THEN THE FATHER OF THE BOY CAME AND CURSED ME IN GRIEF AND ANGER.

WHAT IS THE CURSE?

HE CURSED ME THAT I SHOULD, AS PENANCE, CARRY FROGS ON MY BACK. SO I'VE COME TO CARRY YOU WHEREVER YOU WISH...

...IF YOU'LL KINDLY PERMIT ME.

IS THAT SO? IT'S VERY GOOD OF YOU!

THE FROG TOLD ALL HIS FRIENDS ABOUT THIS STRANGE HAPPENING, AND EVEN WENT TO THE FROG KING...

WONDERFUL! LET'S GO AND HAVE A JOY-RIDE ON THE BACK OF THE BLACK SNAKE!

ALL THE FROGS FOLLOWED THE KING AND WENT TO WHERE MANDAVISHA WAS RESTING.

WELCOME, O NOBLE FROG KING! I AM HERE TO SERVE YOU AND YOUR FOLLOWERS!

CAN I HAVE A RIDE NOW?

CERTAINLY! I CAN GLIDE, I CAN TROT, I CAN GALLOP...CLIMB ON!

THIS IS SIMPLY THRILLING...RIDING ON A SNAKE!

Sandhivigraha

Harmony and Strife

AH! OH!

THIS IS GREAT!

THE NEXT DAY, THE SNAKE PRETENDED TO BE TIRED AND WEAK AND CRAWLED SLOWLY...

MY DEAR MANDAVISHA! WHAT IS THE MATTER WITH YOU? YOU LOOK ILL.

I'M HOPELESSLY WEAK BECAUSE I HAVEN'T EATEN IN THE LAST TWO DAYS.

WHAT A PITY! I SHALL FEED YOU WITH FROGS.

NO, NO, I CAN'T DO THAT! IT'S A SIN!

DON'T WORRY, THEY ARE MY SLAVES AND I OFFER THEM TO YOU.

SO THE SNAKE HAD A SUMPTUOUS MEAL EVERY DAY...

THE PLAN IS WORKING WONDERFULLY WELL!

THE FROG-KING IS A REAL FOOL. HE DOESN'T REALISE THAT HALF OF HIS PEOPLE HAVE BEEN EATEN UP BY ME.

ONE DAY, ANOTHER SNAKE CAME BY...

DEAR BROTHER! IT'S RIDICULOUS AND DISGRACEFUL FOR A SERPENT TO CARRY FROGS ON HIS BACK!

WE MUST DEVOUR THEM, NOT CARRY THEM!

HUSH! I KNOW THIS AS WELL AS YOU. I'M ONLY BIDING MY TIME LIKE THE BRAHMIN WHO HAD AN UNFAITHFUL WIFE.

Sandhivigraha

Harmony and Strife

WHICH BRAHMIN? TELL ME THE STORY!

LONG AGO, THERE WAS A BRAHMIN WHO HAD AN UNFAITHFUL WIFE. SHE USED TO MAKE DAINTY DISHES FOR HER LOVER AND CARRY THEM SECRETLY TO HIM.

ONE DAY...

MY DEAR! WHERE ARE YOU TAKING THAT FOOD?

DON'T YOU KNOW THAT I GO TO THE TEMPLE OF THE GODDESS KALI EVERY DAY AND MAKE OFFERINGS TO HER ACCORDING TO A SACRED VOW?

THE BRAHMIN'S WIFE WENT TO THE TEMPLE THAT DAY TO DECEIVE HER HUSBAND...

I DON'T TRUST HER. I'LL TAKE A SHORT CUT TO THE TEMPLE.

AT THE TEMPLE...

I'LL HIDE HERE BEHIND THE IDOL...AH, THERE SHE IS!

O GODDESS! PRAY MAKE MY HUSBAND BLIND!

I'M PLEASED WITH YOU. I GRANT YOU YOUR PRAYER!

FROM BEHIND THE IDOL, THE BRAHMIN SPOKE...

MAKE SWEETS WITH A LOT OF BUTTER AND SERVE THEM TO HIM EVERY DAY. IN DUE COURSE, HE'LL GO BLIND.

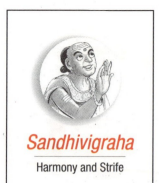

Sandhivigraha
Harmony and Strife

THE FOOLISH WOMAN BELIEVED IT TO BE THE VOICE OF THE GODDESS. EVERY DAY, SHE SPECIALLY PREPARED THE MOST TASTY OF DISHES FOR HER HUSBAND TILL HE GREW FAT AND STRONG. ONE DAY...

DEAR WIFE! OF LATE, MY EYESIGHT IS FAILING ME, AND I'M UNHAPPY.

YOU MUST BE GROWING OLD!

THE DIVINE MOTHER HAS AT LAST GRANTED MY BOON...

NOW I CAN SAFELY BRING MY LOVER HERE!

THE BLACK SNAKE CONCLUDED THE STORY THUS...

THE AUDACIOUS WIFE INVITED HER LOVER TO HER HOUSE BELIEVING HER HUSBAND TO BE BLIND...

THE CLEVER BRAHMIN CAUGHT HOLD OF THE LOVER, GAVE HIM A GOOD THRASHING AND KICKED OUT HIS UNFAITHFUL WIFE.

SO, PLAN WELL, WAIT FOR THE RIGHT MOMENT AND THEN STRIKE...

THE OLD CROW FINISHED HIS NARRATIVE THUS...

THE BLACK SNAKE COULD, THROUGH TACT, GET RID OF ALL ENEMIES...

YES, THAT IS TRUE!

ENEMIES AND DEBT, DISEASE AND FIRE, MUST BE COMPLETELY ELIMINATED.

WITH YOUR INTELLIGENCE, YOU WON THE CONFIDENCE OF THE ENEMY AND WIPED HIM OUT!

O KING! YOU CAN LIVE IN PEACE NOW!

Sandhivigraha

Harmony and Strife

VISHNU SHARMA CAME TO THE END OF **SANDHIVIGRAHA**, THE THIRD PART OF THE **PANCHATANTRA**...

MY DEAR PRINCES, YOU'VE HEARD **SANDHIVIGRAHA**, WHICH ILLUSTRATES STATECRAFT AND ALL ITS FACETS...

SIR, WE ARE VERY GRATEFUL TO YOU.

YOU SEE, IT WAS THE WIT AND WISDOM OF HIS COUNSELLOR THAT BROUGHT VICTORY TO MEGHAVARNA...

THE ULTIMATE VICTORY DEPENDS ON WISDOM, NOT ON THE SWORD.

THE SWORD SLAYS THE FOE BUT STRATEGY WIPES OUT EVERYTHING THAT HE POSSESSES...

DISCRETION, THE SPIRIT OF SACRIFICE AND VALOUR ARE THE QUALITIES OF A GOOD KING...

NOW LISTEN TO **LABDHANASA**, THE FOURTH PART OF THE **PANCHATANTRA**, WHICH ILLUSTRATES HOW GAINS CAN BE LOST THROUGH LACK OF DISCRETION.

WE'RE EAGER TO HEAR THESE STORIES, SIR!

ONCE, THERE WAS AN OLD MONKEY NAMED BALIVARDHA. HE LIVED BY THE SEASHORE ON AN UDUMBARA TREE...

ONE DAY, A CROCODILE CALLED KRAKACHA CAME OUT OF THE SEA TO REST UNDER THE SHADE OF THE TREE...